Hey! What's the name of this book?

Bernice myers' Book
of
Giggles

SCHOLASTIC INC.

New York Toronto London Auckland Sydney

I wonder if she dedicated it to me?

ISBN 0-590-30067-9

Copyright © 1979 by Bernice Myers. All rights reserved. Published by Scholastic Inc.

12 11 10 9 8 7 6 5 4   5 6 7 8/8

Printed in the U.S.A.   28

It's dedicated to
Mary Jane Dunton
and everyone at Lucky Books.

What do you
want to be
when you
grow up?

Taller.

Are you flying to outer-space?

No!

Landing.

Then what are you doing in that spaceship?

meOW

15

Hey, Sue!
How did you get
the people next door
to stop complaining
about your violin?

I began
playing
the drums!

Once I swallowed my father's pen.

That's awful. What happened?

He had to use a pencil.

THE PICNIC

It's hot
up
here.

Open
a window.

THE FLYING LESSON

How did you get your parents to let you keep the dog you found?

I dressed
him like my
Uncle Sidney.

There's no
such thing.

Now he
tells me!

44

·THE NEW PUPPY·

Wake up
in time!

I can't stand
the noise from
the helicopter.

Put
cotton wool
in your
ears.

I'm the 6-headed giant.

But you only have 5 heads!

...and if I'm not telling the truth may a striped one-legged Bald Eagle with a purple wig fall on my head...